Unit 4
Islamic Empires in the Middle Ages
Activity Book

GRADE 4

Core Knowledge Language Arts®

Core Knowledge®

Amplify.

ISBN 978-1-942010-08-1

Unit 4
Islamic Empires in the Middle Ages
Activity Book

This Activity Book contains activity pages that accompany the lessons from the Unit 4 Teacher Guide. The activity pages are organized and numbered according to the lesson number and the order in which they are used within the lesson. For example, if there are two activity pages for Lesson 4, the first will be numbered 4.1 and the second 4.2. The Activity Book is a student component, which means each student should have an Activity Book.

Reading

Four of the territories that you learned about are listed above the map below. Draw a line from each of them to the correct star on the map. Then answer questions 1–5.

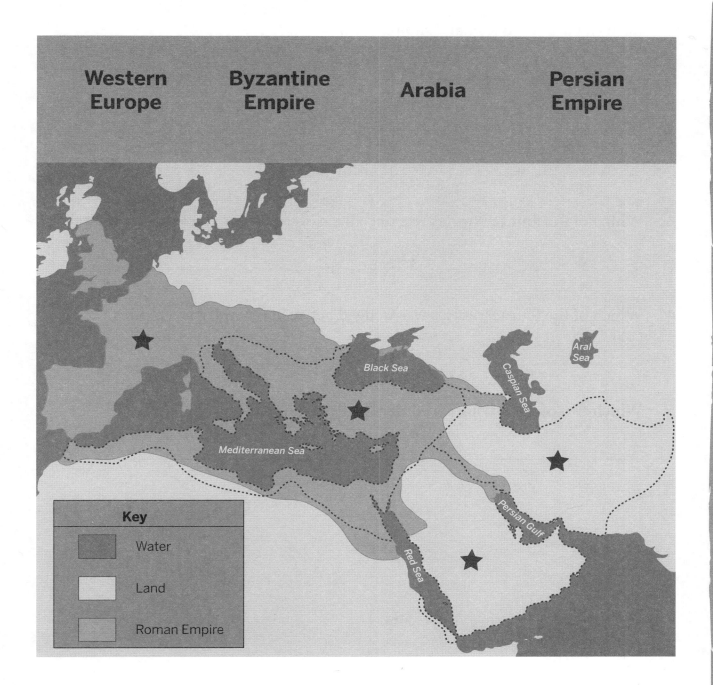

Use the map on page 1 to answer these questions.

1. The countries of _____ developed on land that was once the western part of the Roman Empire.

   _____

2. Which of the four territories is the farthest east?

   _____

3. Which of the four territories was once the eastern part of the Roman Empire?

   _____

4. Which of the four territories was wedged between two warring empires?

   _____

5. Which two of the territories border the Persian Gulf?

   _____

Reading

1. What became of the western and eastern territories that once made up the Roman Empire?

   _____

   _____

   _____

2. What was the relationship between the Byzantine Empire and the Persian (or Sasanian) Empire?

   _____

   _____

   _____

3. What goods were traded between the West and the East?

   _____

   _____

   _____

4. What does *monotheistic* mean?

   _____

   _____

5. How do camels keep unwanted people or animals away from them?

_____

_____

_____

6. **Challenge**: Words that have more than one syllable are called <u>polysyllabic</u>. Examples of polysyllabic words are *empire*, which has two syllables (em-pire) and *elephant*, which has three syllables (e-le-phant). What word do you think describes words of one syllable?

_____

7. **Challenge**: Write two sentences using the word *rival.*

_____

_____

_____

8. **Challenge**: Write a sentence using your favorite word in the glossary.

_____

_____

1. **emerged**, *n*. developed (**3**)

2. **dominated**, *n*. ruled (**3**)

3. **caravans**, *n*. groups of merchants traveling together (**4**)

4. **merchants**, *n*. people who buy and sell things for profit (**5**)

5. **diverse**, *adj*. including many kinds (**6**)

6. **monotheistic**, *adj*. believing in a single god (**6**)

7. **arid**, *adj*. very dry (**6**)

8. **shrine**, *n*. a place that people visit to remember or worship a god or religious figure (**6**)

9. **domestication**, *n*. the process of training animals to live with, or work for, people (**7**)

10. **conquests**, *n*. when things or places are acquired through force (**7**)

Reading

1. The text says Muhammad was believed to have been illiterate (unable to read and write) but that he "understood the importance of words and stories." How do you think Muhammad might have gained this understanding during his time among the Bedouins? Provide evidence from the text.

   _____

   _____

   _____

2. Write two sentences comparing two different features of the lives of children in Muhammad's time to your life today.

   First Sentence:

   _____

   _____

   Second Sentence:

   _____

   _____

3. How did Muhammad's life in Mecca differ from his life among the Bedouins?

   _____

   _____

Reading

Read the following passage, which describes life traveling in the desert with a caravan.

> The desert was scorching in the day and freezing at night. Most people walked for hundreds of miles, as camels were needed to carry the goods. During the day they had to watch for raiders who would attack caravans and leave the people to die. At night, people took turns keeping watch for wolves, hyenas, or thieves attempting to steal the camels.

Using facts from the passage, write a paragraph in the first-person describing the experience of a person traveling with a caravan.

_____

_____

_____

_____

_____

_____

NAME: _____ DATE: _____

Grammar

Sentence Fragments

Indicate whether each of the following sentences or phrases is a complete sentence or a sentence fragment. Rewrite the sentence fragments as complete sentences by adding a subject or predicate.

Example: Shivered in the cold night air.

_____ Complete sentence

__X__ Sentence fragment

The men shivered in the cold night air. _____

1. The spitting camel

    _____ Complete sentence

    _____ Sentence fragment

    _____

2. The camel and the hyena were good friends

    _____ Complete sentence

    _____ Sentence fragment

    _____

3. Eleven camels outside the tent

    _____ Complete sentence

    _____ Sentence fragment

    _____

4. The Bedouin boy chased the camel

   _____ Complete sentence

   _____ Sentence fragment

   _____

5. By selling his wares, the merchant earned money to buy a camel

   _____ Complete sentence

   _____ Sentence fragment

   _____

6. All the camels marching through the desert

   _____ Complete sentence

   _____ Sentence fragment

   _____

7. The camel spat at the Bedouin boy

   _____ Complete sentence

   _____ Sentence fragment

   _____

8. The difficult life of a caravan camel

   _____ Complete sentence

   _____ Sentence fragment

   _____

Challenge: Circle the subject and underline the predicate of each complete sentence above.

Morphology

un– and *non*–: Prefixes Meaning "Not"

Under each of the following sentences, write a new sentence using the word written in parentheses.

Example: Writing **fiction** lets me use my imagination. (nonfiction)

He reads nonfiction to learn about the real world.

1. Plants and animals are all **living** beings. (nonliving)

   _____

   _____

2. I like to give gifts, but I don't like to **wrap** them. (unwrap)

   _____

   _____

3. Playing cards with Grandpa is a **pleasant** way to spend an afternoon. (unpleasant)

   _____

   _____

4. Water is **essential** to staying alive, but is sometimes hard to find in the desert. (nonessential)

   _____

   _____

Morphology

en–: Prefix Meaning "to make"

Choose the correct word, and write it in to complete the sentence.

1. I know we'll _____ our day at the beach.
    (joy, enjoy, courage, encourage)

2. The salesman hoped that smiling would _____ him
    to customers.   (case, encase, dear, endear)

3. I packed an extra bottle of water to _____that I would not be
    thirsty during the hike.   (force, enforce, sure, ensure)

4. It took a lot of _____for Emily to audition for the
    school play.   (courage, encourage, circle, encircle)

5. The school _____ all the trophies behind glass.
    (sure, ensured, case, encased)

6. Hoping to _____ myself, I dug for gold in my backyard.
    (able, enable, rich, enrich)

2.6
Writing

NAME: _____ DATE: _____

Lands and Empires Graphic Organizer

Subjects	Quotes from the Reader
Roman Empire	p. 3 "The Roman Empire had dominated for centuries. It had covered land that over forty different countries occupy today." p. 4 "Many believed it would last forever. They were wrong."
Byzantine Empire	
Persian Empire	
Arabia	

Notes for Paraphrasing

NAME: _____ DATE: _____

1. **inauspicious**, *adj.* not suggesting future success (**8**)

2. **Bedouins**, *n.* Arabic people who live in the desert (**8**)

3. **predators,** *n.* animals that hunt other animals (**9**)

4. **plummets**, *v.* drops very fast (**9**)

5. **oral,** *adj.* related to speaking or voice (**9**)

6. **bustling**, *v.* hurrying; moving fast and with purpose (**10**)

7. **wares,** *n.* goods or products that a merchant or shop sells (**10**)

8. **vulnerable**, *adj.* weak; helpless (**11**)

9. **scorching**, *adj.* very hot (**11**)

10. **raiders**, *n.* robbers (**11**)

11. **humble**, *adj.* modest, not extravagant (**11**)

12. **reputation,** *n.* the opinion people hold about something or someone (**11**)

13. **integrity**, *n.* honesty (**11**)

Reading

Map Activity

On the lines below, fill in the events that took place in the years listed. Then, on the map on the following page, draw a line from each event to the city where it took place.

610: <u>Muhammad had his first vision.</u> _____

613: _____

619: _____

622: _____

630: _____

632: _____

NAME: _____ DATE: _____

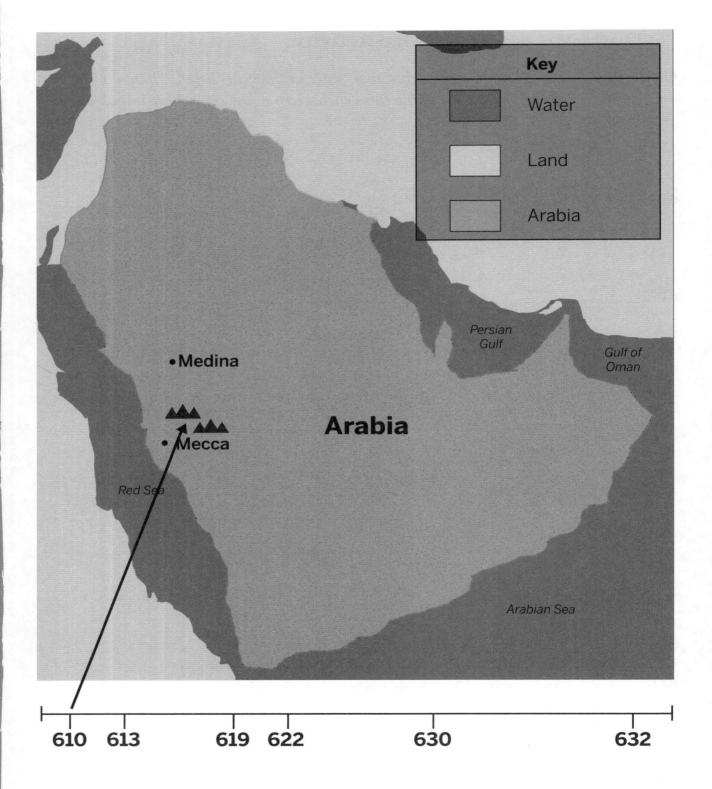

Writing

Below are nine events in the life of Muhammad. Write a number next to each event to show the order in which the events occurred. To help you get started, three events have already been given numbers.

_____ Muhammad was born.

_____ Muhammad was sent to live in the desert.

___9_____ Muhammad became a close advisor to his uncle.

___5_____ Muhammad returned to Mecca.

___1_____ Muhammad's father died.

_____ Muhammad worked for his uncle as a camel boy.

_____ Muhammad's mother died.

_____ Muhammad's grandfather died.

_____ Muhammad worked for the Bedouins.

3.3

Writing

Muhammad's Childhood Graphic Organizer

Subjects	Quotes from the Reader
Birth and Infancy	
Life among the Bedouins	
Return to Mecca	

Paraphrased Notes	Full-sentence Paraphrases (Detail Sentences)

NAME: _____ DATE: _____

1. **solitude,** *n.* being alone (**12**)

2. **recitation,** *n.* something spoken from memory (**recite**) (**12**)

3. **scribes,** *n.* people who copied documents before modern printing was invented (**12**)

4. **compiled,** *v.* put different texts together into a book (**12**)

5. **pilgrimage,** *n.* a journey to a place or shrine that is important to a religion (**12**)

6. **preaching,** *v.* speaking publicly, usually about religion (**13**)

7. **revelations,** *n.* the acts of a god revealing himself or herself (or his or her will) to a person (**13**)

8. **blasphemy,** *n.* words or actions that are offensive to a religion (**13**)

9. **persecution,** *n.* the mistreatment of a person or group (**14**)

10. **bleak,** *adj.* hopeless; depressing (**14**)

11. **arbiter,** *n.* a person with the authority to settle disputes (**14**)

12. **tactics,** *n.* procedures employed to gain success (**15**)

13. **acknowledge,** *v.* accept; recognize (**15**)

14. **pardoned,** *v.* forgave (**15**)

15. **humiliated,** *v.* caused a person or people to lose their dignity or self-respect (**15**)

16. **authority,** *n.* a source of information that people believe is correct (**15**)

17. **sermon,** *n.* a speech for the purpose of religious instruction (**18**)

18. **idols,** *n.* a statue or image worshipped as a god or as the representation of a god (**18**)

19. **mosque,** *n.* a place where Muslims worship (**18**)

20. **ambiguity,** *n.* uncertainty of meaning or intention (**19**)

21. **discord,** *n.* disagreement (**19**)

Reading

The Genius of Umar

The Reader refers to Umar as "a political genius." Below is a list of actions Umar took while in power. Under each, explain why the act might be considered "political genius."

Example:

He appointed regional governors.

This could be seen as political genius because:

It shows that Umar realized he needed strong people under him

to rule the very large empire.

1. He required officials to live in a humble way and keep their doors open to all the people.

    This could be seen as political genius because:

    _____

    _____

2. He lived in a small home and wore inexpensive clothes.

    This could be seen as political genius because:

    _____

    _____

3. He investigated complaints against officials and punished those who broke the rules.

    This could be seen as political genius because:

    _____

    _____

NAME: _____   DATE: _____

Reading

1. Name the first three caliphs after Muhammad's death.

    _____

    _____

2. How was Abu Bakr related to Muhammad?

    _____

3. The Reader states on page 36 that Abu Bakr realized "the times became too dangerous for the holy book to live only in people's heads." In what way were the times "too dangerous"? You may want to re-read "The codification of the Qur'an" on page 36 to help you answer this question.

    _____

    _____

    _____

4. Write a paragraph that paraphrases "The story of Umar's conversion to Islam," on page 23.

    _____

    _____

    _____

    _____

    _____

Reading

Run-on Sentences

There are three run-on sentences in the paragraph below. Read the paragraph, and underline and number each of the run-on sentences. Remember to number only the run-on sentences. On the next page, rewrite each of the run-on sentences as two separate sentences, using proper punctuation and capitalization.

Example:

The camel drank at the oasis she was very thirsty. [*1*]

Possible Answer:

The camel drank at the oasis. She was very thirsty .

Hamid was a remarkable little boy. [   ] He was born into a very poor Bedouin tribe. [   ] He started working at the age of three his job was to feed and water the camels. [   ] He liked living in the desert, but a few years later his family moved to Mecca. [   ] Mecca was a noisy place compared with the desert. [   ] The streets were filled with merchants and shopkeepers shouting there were also many poor people. [   ] Hamid sold jewelry in an outdoor marketplace in Mecca. [   ] Eventually he became a successful merchant he married a Bedouin girl from his tribe. [   ]

1. Correction of Run-on Sentence 1:

_____

_____

_____

2. Correction of Run-on Sentence 2:

_____

_____

_____

3. Correction of Run-on Sentence 3:

_____

_____

_____

Morphology

Root Word: *arch*

Vocabulary Words

1. **patriarch**, *n.* a man who controls a family or community
2. **matriarch**, *n.* a woman who controls a family or community
3. **archbishop**, *n.* a high-ranking church official
4. **monarch,** *n.* a ruler
5. **archenemy,** *n.* a chief enemy
6. **hierarchy,** *n.* a system in which people are placed into different levels of power and importance
7. **archrival**, *n.* a chief rival
8. **anarchy,** *n.* a system with no leader that is not controlled by rules or laws
9. **archduke,** *n.* a high-ranking noble

From the words listed below, choose the one that best completes each sentence.

monarchy	hierarchy	archenemy	patriarch
	archduke	anarchy	

1. As _____ of the family, Uncle Ezra always carved the Thanksgiving turkey.

2. The vampire hunter thought of the vampire as his _____.

3. I believe that even an imperfect government is better than _____.

4. So long as the king was fair and kind, we didn't mind living in a _____.

5. In the _____ of the Islamic empire, the caliph was the most powerful leader.

6. The king often consulted the _____ before making decisions that would impact the other nobles.

7. Write a complete sentence using the word *matriarch*.

    _____

    _____

8. **Challenge**: Based on what you have learned about the root *arch*, what do you think the word *archangel* means?

    _____

    _____

1. **caliph**, *n.* an Islamic spiritual and religious leader claiming succession from Muhammad (**21**)

2. **formidable**, *adj.* powerful (**22**)

3. **campaign**, *n.* multiple military actions (**22**)

4. **peninsula**, *n.* an area of land surrounded by water on three sides (**22**)

5. **exploited**, *v.* used selfishly (**22**)

6. **nominated,** *v.* appointed (**22**)

7. **assassinated**, *v.* killed on purpose (**23**)

8. **flaunting**, *v.* showing off (**24**)

9. **dismissed**, v. fired, as from a job (**24**)

10. **flogged**, *v.* whipped (**24**)

11. **devastated**, *v.* caused great destruction to (**25**)

12. **controversial**, *adj.* open to dispute (**35**)

13. **predecessors**, *n.* people who came before another (**35**)

14. **pious**, *adj.* following a religion with dedication (**35**)

15. **lavish**, *adj.* fancy and expensive (**35**)

NAME: _____   DATE: _____

Reading

If you have been assigned the role of infantrymen, fill in the "Infantry" row of the organizer below. If you have been assigned the role of cavalry, fill in the "Cavalry" row.

Type of soldier	In training they are...	In battle they will...
Infantry		
Cavalry		

Are there any other soldiers mentioned?	What are these other soldiers doing in training?	What are these other soldiers doing in battle?

5.2

NAME: _____   DATE: _____

Writing

Topic Sentence:

_____

_____

Detail Sentences:

1. _____

_____

2. _____

_____

3. _____

_____

4. _____

_____

5. _____

_____

Concluding Sentence:

_____

_____

Writing

First Draft of Your Full Paragraph

_____

_____

_____

_____

_____

_____

_____

_____

_____

_____

_____

_____

Revision Ideas

1. *Try adding transition words like* additionally, further, next, then, also, first, second, *and* finally.

2. *Try substituting a pronoun for a proper name to give your sentences variety. Examples of pronouns are* he, his, she, *and* her.

3. *Try adding emphasis word like* certainly, really, very, surely, *or* definitely, *especially in your concluding sentence.*

NAME: _____   DATE: _____

Revised Draft of Your Full Paragraph

_____

_____

_____

_____

_____

_____

_____

_____

_____

_____

_____

1. **savvy**, *adj.* knowledgeable and clever (**26**)

2. **unbearable,** *adj.* unable to be tolerated (**27**)

3. **infantrymen**, *n.* soldiers who fight on foot (**28**)

4. **cavalry,** *n.* soldiers riding horses (**28**)

5. **crude**, *adj.* impolite (**28**)

6. **jostling**, *v.* bumping and pushing in a rough way (**28**)

7. **arrogance**, *n.* showing extreme pride or self-importance (**28**)

8. **long-swords**, *n.* types of swords designed for two-handed use (**28**)

9. **duels**, *n.* combat between two people that is planned in advance (**28**)

10. **suppressed**, *v.* kept a feeling inside (**29**)

11. **twinge**, *n.* a sudden, sharp feeling or emotion (**29**)

Reading

Annotate the Diagram

Annotate the diagram in your activity book that applies to the day you have been assigned. Take each sentence in the text that describes an "action," and copy it underneath the diagram. Then draw a line from the sentence to the arrow or symbol on the diagram that represents it.

An example is below:

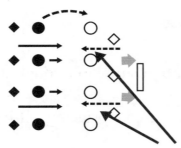

"Their fury forced their husbands back into the battle."

Day 2

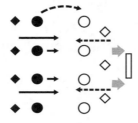

_____

_____

_____

_____

Day 3

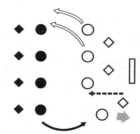

_____

_____

_____

_____

Day 4

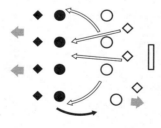

_____

_____

_____

_____

6.1

NAME: _____ DATE: _____

Day 6

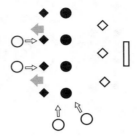

_____

_____

_____

_____

_____

Grammar

The Four Sentence Types

For items 1–10, circle the correct sentence type.

> **Declarative Sentence** – a simple statement
>
> **Interrogative Sentence** – a question
>
> **Imperative Sentence** – a command or order
>
> **Exclamatory Sentence** – a statement expressing excitement or emotion

1. Pass the pickles.

    declarative   interrogative   imperative   exclamatory

2. What time did you wake up?

    declarative   interrogative   imperative   exclamatory

3. I'll be home before dark.

    declarative   interrogative   imperative   exclamatory

4. That is the funniest thing I ever heard in my entire life!

    declarative   interrogative   imperative   exclamatory

5. You're drinking poison!

    declarative   interrogative   imperative   exclamatory

6. Who made you the boss?

    declarative   interrogative   imperative   exclamatory

7. Ignore your sister.

    declarative   interrogative   imperative   exclamatory

8. I read that book last year.

    declarative   interrogative   imperative   exclamatory

9. Abraham Lincoln invented mayonnaise.

    declarative   interrogative   imperative   exclamatory

10. There's a shark in the pool!

    declarative   interrogative   imperative   exclamatory

11. Write an example of each of the four sentence types.

    Declarative Sentence:

    _____

    _____

    _____

    Interrogative Sentence:

    _____

    _____

    _____

Imperative Sentence:

_____

_____

_____

Exclamatory Sentence:

_____

_____

_____

6.3

NAME: _____ DATE: _____

Morphology

Root Word: *graph*

Vocabulary Words

1. **autobiography**, *n.* a nonfiction book someone writes about his or her own life
2. **autograph**, *n.* a person's signature
3. **bibliography**, *n.* a list of books and texts consulted in writing a paper
4. **biography**, *n.* a nonfiction book about someone's life
5. **calligraphy**, *n.* the art of decorative handwriting
6. **cartography**, *n.* the art of designing and making maps
7. **choreography**, *n.* the planned movements of dancers
8. **graph**, *n.* a diagram that represents the relationship between two or more things
9. **graphic**, *n.* an image, sometimes accompanying text
10. **graphite**, *n.* a mineral used in pencils
11. **paragraph**, *n.* a section of a written work, usually composed of multiple sentences
12. **phonograph**, *n.* a machine that plays sound recordings
13. **photograph**, *n.* an image produced by taking a picture
14. **telegraph**, *n.* a machine for transmitting messages over a long distance

For items 1–8, choose the one that best completes each sentence.

paragraph	bibliography	calligraphy	autobiography
graphite	choreography	cartographer	telegraph

1. A few students had some trouble learning the difficult _____

   for the school musical.

2. _____ has replaced lead as the core of most pencils.

3. The _____ worked for years on her atlas of the new world.

4. The main point of a newspaper article is often found in the first or second

   _____.

5. Fatima admired the beautiful _____with which her copy of

   the Qur'an was written.

6. Herbie thought that others would enjoy reading about his experiences, so he

   wrote his _____.

7. Cecelia listed eight books in the _____of her report on the

   animals of Arabia.

8. Until the townspeople had telephones installed, their messages were sent by Old

   Clem over a _____ .

9. Write a complete sentence using the word *photograph*.

   _____

   _____

10. Write a complete sentence using the word *autograph*.

   _____

   _____

6.4

NAME: _____   DATE: _____

Spelling

Below is a list of spelling words from the Reader.

During Lesson 10, you will be assessed on how to spell these words. Practice spelling them by doing one or more of the following:

- Spell the words aloud.
- Write sentences using the words.
- Copy the words onto paper.
- Write the words in alphabetical order.

When you practice spelling and writing the words, remember to pronounce and spell each word one syllable at a time.

1. collapse _____

2. diverse _____

3. hyena _____

4. integrity _____

5. illiterate _____

6. conquest _____

7. governor _____

8. guilty _____

9. humiliate _____

10. fray _____

The following chart provides the meanings of the spelling words. You will not be assessed on the definitions, but it may be helpful to have them as a reference as you practice spelling the words throughout the week.

Spelling Word	Definition
collapse	*v.* to break down or crumble
diverse	*adj.* having different kinds
hyena	*n.* a dog-like carnivore with large teeth
integrity	*n.* honesty
illiterate	*adj.* unable to read or write
conquest	*n.* a gain through the use of force
governor	*n.* a person in charge of a state or territory
guilty	*adj.* having committed a crime or offense
humiliate	*v.* to embarrass or cause someone to lose dignity
fray	*n.* a battle

6.5

NAME: _____ DATE: _____

Spelling

Write a sentence of the type indicated using the following spelling words.

1. Word: *humiliate*

    Sentence type: interrogative

    _____

    _____

2. Word: *guilty*

    Sentence type: interrogative

    _____

    _____

3. Word: *governor*

    Sentence type: declarative

    _____

    _____

4.   Word: *conquest*

Sentence type: exclamatory

_____

_____

5.   Word: *illiterate*

Sentence type: declarative

_____

_____

6.   Word: *integrity*

Sentence type: declarative

_____

_____

7.   Word: *hyena*

Sentence type: exclamatory

_____

_____

8. Word: *diverse*

    Sentence type: declarative

    _____

    _____

9. Word: *collapse*

    Sentence type: exclamatory

    _____

    _____

10. Word: *fray*

    Sentence type: imperative

    _____

    _____

1. **ploy**, *n.* a maneuver designed to fool an enemy (**30**)

2. **overwhelmed,** *v.* felt unable to handle a situation (**30**)

3. **thwarted,** *v.* prevented from accomplishing something (**30**)

4. **retired,** *v.* went to bed (**30**)

5. **fray,** *n.* battle (**31**)

6. **havoc,** *n.* confusion (**31**)

7. **blow,** *n.* a sudden attack (**32**)

8. **outwitted**, *v.* outsmarted (**32**)

9. **three-pronged**, *adj.* three-part (**32**)

10. **maneuver,** *n.* a planned movement of troops (**32**)

11. **self-loathing**, *n.* a feeling of disgust about oneself (**33**)

12. **courier**, *n.* messenger (**33**)

13. **truce**, *n.* an agreement that puts an end to fighting (**33**)

NAME: _____   DATE: _____

Reading

The Caliph Review

1. The six caliphs who succeeded Muhammad are listed below. In the spaces provided, list the caliphs in the chronological order of their reigns. Then circle the caliphs who were his relatives.

Uthman	Abu Bakr	Ali	Umar	Muawiyah	Hasan

Muhammad

1. _____

2. _____

3. _____

4. _____

5. _____

6. _____

2. Identify the caliph described in the following clues.

A. He was criticized for failing to punish his predecessor's assassins.

caliph: _____

B. He united the entire Arabian Peninsula for the first time.

caliph: _____

C. He was the only one of the first six caliphs to retire.

caliph: _____

D. He founded the Umayyad dynasty.

caliph: _____

E. He was caliph during the Battle of Yarmouk.

caliph: _____

F. Under his rule, the final, "official" version of the Qur'an was codified.

caliph: _____

NAME: _____ DATE: _____

Reading

1. Who led the opposing sides at the start of the Muslim civil war?

   _____

   _____

   _____

2. What were the two sides fighting over?

   _____

   _____

   _____

   _____

3. Why was the Islamic civil war more traumatic for Muslims than the wars against the Byzantine Empire?

   _____

   _____

   _____

   _____

Writing

Story Elements

1. Write down the setting of one of your favorite books. If possible, include the location and time period in which the story takes place.

    Book title: _____

    When the story takes place: _____

    Where the story takes place: _____

2. Who is the protagonist of one of your favorite books? Try to provide a physical trait and a personality trait.

    Book title: _____

    Name of protagonist: _____

    Protagonist's physical trait: _____

    Protagonist's personality trait: _____

3. What is the protagonist's <u>want</u> in one of your favorite books?

    _____

    _____

    _____

    _____

4. What <u>obstacle</u> might prevent Jack from solving his want?

_____

_____

_____

_____

5. Describe a possible <u>resolution</u> to Jack's story.

_____

_____

_____

_____

Writing

Details for My Story

Subject	Detail
Water	Finding enough water in the desert to survive was a struggle.
Food	
Work	Children tended to the camels.
Dangers	
Temperature	
Nighttime	Men recited long poems about battles and adventures.

7.5

Writing

NAME: _____ DATE: _____

Historical Fiction Story Organizer

Story Element	Your Story
Setting	The Arabian desert in the year 560.
Protagonist	
Protagonist's Want	
Obstacle	
Resolution	

1. **nepotistic**, *adj.* granting special favors to relatives and friends **(39)**

2. **opposition**, *n.* a group of people who are against something **(39)**

3. **traumatic,** *adj.* emotionally painful **(39)**

4. **garrison town,** *n.* a town that is protected, perhaps by a wall **(39)**

5. **schism,** *n.* division; split **(41)**

6. **resounded,** *v.* echoed and repeated **(41)**

7. **consensus**, *n.* agreement between different people or groups **(42)**

Reading

1. Whom do the Shia believe should have been caliph after the civil war?

   _____

   _____

   _____

2. Whom do the Sunni believe should have been caliph after the civil war?

   _____

   _____

   _____

3. What is Shia short for?

   _____

   _____

   _____

4. Why was the Umayyad dynasty unusual?

   _____

   _____

   _____

   _____

5. Where in the world during the Middle Ages were family dynasties common?

    _____

    _____

    _____

6. What did the Umayyad Caliphate contribute to the empire?

    _____

    _____

    _____

NAME: _____   DATE: _____

Reading

1. What was unusual about Muawiyah's appointment of his successor as caliph?

    _____

    _____

    _____

    _____

2. What event from the year 680 do Shiite Muslims still mourn, or remember sadly, to this day?

    _____

    _____

    _____

    _____

3. Why did the expansion of the Islamic empire stop during the early days of the Umayyad dynasty?

    _____

    _____

    _____

    _____

Writing

Historical Fiction Writing Tips

A. First-person vs. Third-person

A story told in the first-person is narrated by a character. A story told in the third-person is told by someone who is not a character.

Example of First-person Narration:

I decided to spit right back at the next camel that spat at me.

Example of Third-person Narration:

The girl decided she would spit right back at the next camel that spat at her.

B. Use Specific Verbs

Write down three words you could use instead of *went* in the following sentence:
Omar went to his tent without talking to anyone.

Example: *marched*

1. _____

2. _____

3. _____

C. Unique Voices

Everyone has his or her own way of speaking. When you are writing dialogue for a character, think about that character's unique voice.

How might the following characters ask for a cup of tea from a merchant in the marketplace? Write what you think they might say.

1. A grumpy grandfather who buys tea from the merchant every day:

   _____

   _____

   _____

   _____

2. A shy Bedouin child who is in a big city for the first time:

   _____

   _____

   _____

   _____

3. A busy caravan leader who is running late:

   _____

   _____

   _____

   _____

Writing

My Work of Historical Fiction

Title: _____

Story: _____

_____

_____

_____

_____

_____

_____

_____

_____

_____

_____

_____

_____

8.4

NAME: _____ DATE: _____

_____

_____

_____

_____

_____

_____

_____

_____

_____

_____

_____

_____

1. **discontented**, *adj.* unhappy; not satisfied (**41**)

2. **massacre**, *n.* the killing of a large number of people (**42**)

3. **martyrdom**, *n.* death or suffering for the sake of a cause or belief (**42**)

4. **triumphant**, *adj.* victorious (**42**)

5. **unity**, *n.* absence of disagreement (**43**)

6. **sacred**, *adj.* holy (**43**)

7. **potent**, *adj.* powerful (**43**)

8. **plausible**, *adj.* seems worthy of acceptance (**44**)

9. **milestones**, *n.* stones marking the distance to some place (**45**)

10. **architectural**, *adj.* relating to the design and construction of buildings (**architecture**) (**45**)

11. **masterpieces**, *n.* great works of art (**masterpiece**) (**45**)

12. **ascended**, *v.* rose; went upward (**46**)

13. **modifications**, *n.* changes (**47**)

14. **arches**, *n.* openings or gateways that are curved on top (**arch**) (**47**)

15. **alternately**, *adv.* switching regularly and repeatedly (**47**)

16. **interior,** *n.* the inside of something (**47**)

17. **distinctive**, *adj.* different; unique (**47**)

18. **countless,** *adj.* too many to count (**47**)

Grammar

For each item, write a sentence that is of the type indicated and that uses the word provided.

Example:

> Sentence Type: declarative
> Word: *spinach*
>
> The spinach will be on sale tomorrow.

1. Sentence Type: declarative
    Word: *pony*

    _____

    _____

2. Sentence Type: interrogative
    Word: *lighthouse*

    _____

    _____

3. Sentence Type: imperative
    Word: *burn*

    _____

    _____

4. Sentence Type: exclamatory
    Word: *mosquito*

    _____

    _____

5. Sentence Type: imperative
    Word: *mosquito*

    _____

    _____

6. Sentence Type: exclamatory
    Word: *fog*

    _____

    _____

7. Sentence Type: declarative
    Word: *illiterate*

    _____

    _____

8. Sentence Type: interrogative
    Word: *olive*

    _____

    _____

NAME: _____   DATE: _____

9. Sentence Type: declarative
    Word: *bear*

    _____

    _____

10. Sentence Type: exclamatory
    Word: *scorching*

    _____

    _____

11. **Challenge**
    Sentence Type: declarative sentence containing a question
    Word: *caravan*

    _____

    _____

Morphology

For items 1-4, write a sentence using the word provided.

1. Word: *biography*

   _____

   _____

2. Word: *paragraph*

   _____

   _____

3. Word: *bibliography*

   _____

   _____

4. Word: *graphic*

   _____

   _____

For items 5–8, write a sentence using one of four words provided—except write a blank instead of writing the word you chose. After completing items 5–8, swap activity books with a partner and have him or her figure out which of the four words best completes your sentence.

For example, for item 5, if you chose the word *cartography*, you might write the following sentence, being careful to insert a blank instead of *cartography*:

"Because of his interest in maps, he decided to

write a report on _____."

Your partner would then have to choose *cartography* as the word that best completes your sentence.

5.   Word choices: *biography, calligraphy, cartography, graphite*

_____

_____

The word that best completes my partner's sentence is: _____.

6.   Word choices: *graph, choreography, autograph, calligraphy*

_____

_____

The word that best completes my partner's sentence is: _____.

7. Word choices: *biography, bibliography, cartography, phonograph*

_____

_____

The word that best completes my partner's sentence is: _____.

8. Word choices: *photography, telegraph, graphite, autobiography*

_____

_____

The word that best completes my partner's sentence is: _____.

9.3

Spelling

Practice Using Spelling Words

For questions 1–4, circle the part speech of each of the words provided.

1. *guilty*:   verb   noun   adjective

2. *diverse*:   verb   noun   adjective

3. *integrity*:   verb   noun   adjective

4. *conquest*: verb   noun   adjective

For questions 5–9, use the spelling words provided in a complete sentence. Note that question 9 asks you to use two spelling words in a complete sentence.

5. Word: *collapse*

_____

_____

6. Word: *governor*

_____

_____

7. Word: *humiliate*

_____

_____

8. Word: *illiterate*

_____

_____

9. Words: *hyena – fray*

_____

_____

NAME: _____   DATE: _____

1. **descended,** *v.* had a specific family or person among one's ancestors (**49**)

2. **prosperous,** *adj.* successful (**49**)

3. **flourished,** *v.* was successful and widespread (**49**)

4. **courtyards,** *n.* yards that are open to the sky but enclosed on the sides (**49**)

5. **subtly**, *adv.* in a way that is complicated and pleasant (**49**)

6. **storehouses,** *n.* warehouses'. places where things are stored (**51**)

7. **manuscripts,** *n.* books or documents (**51**)

8. **geometric,** *adj.* patterned with shapes (**53**)

9. **imposing,** *adj.* impressive (**55**)

10. **graceful**, *adj.* beautiful; elegant (**55**)

11. **inspired,** *v.* produced a feeling or thought in someone (**55**)

12. **awe,** *n.* a feeling of being very impressed (**55**)

13. **inscribed,** *v.* engraved (**55**)

14. **interlocked,** *v.* connected (**55**)

15. **infinite,** *adj.* going on forever (**55**)

16. **expanse,** *n.* a vast space (**55**)

17. **elaborate,** *adj.* fancy and detailed (**56**)

18. **tranquility,** *n.* a state of calm (**56**)

19. **intertwined,** *v.* connected (**56**)

20. **spiral,** *adj.* long and winding (**56**)

Spelling

NAME: _____ DATE: _____

Spelling Assesment

Write the spelling words as your teacher calls them out.

1. _____

2. _____

3. _____

4. _____

5. _____

6. _____

7. _____

8. _____

9. _____

10. _____

Reading

Mathematics and Medicine

Use the below key for Roman numerals to answer item 1.

Roman Numerals "Normal" Numerals

I	1
II	2
III	3
IV	4
V	5
VI	6
VII	7
VIII	8
IX	9
X	10
L	50
C	100
D	500
M	1000

Roman numerals are written using the fewest symbols possible. So, for example, 17 is written as XVII and not as VVVII, XIIIIIII, or any other combination.

1. Write the current year in Roman numerals, and then in "normal" numerals (also known as Arabic numerals). Which is easier, and why?

    a. Current year _____

    b. Current year in Roman numerals _____

    c. Writing the year in _____ (Arabic numbers or Roman numerals) is

       easier because _____.

2. What mathematician do we have to thank for not having to do all our math in Roman numerals?

    _____

    _____

3. In what areas, aside from mathematics, did al-Khwarizmi make important discoveries?

    _____

    _____

    _____

4. In mathematics, an algorithm sets out a series of specific steps that can be used to solve a problem. The word *algorithm* comes from a Latin word *algorisme*, which comes from a slightly odd pronunciation of al-Khwarizmi's name. If you try saying *al-Khwarizmi* and *algorisme*, you will hear that the words sound similar to each other. What does the fact that a very important mathematical concept is named after al-Khwarizmi tell us about his work?

_____

_____

_____

_____

5. Write two to three sentences contrasting the cleanliness of Medieval Europe to the cleanliness of the medieval Islamic world.

_____

_____

_____

_____

6. Using full sentences, can you describe at least one important discovery of Ibn Sina's and one important discovery of Abu al-Qasim Al-Zahrawi's?

_____

_____

_____

7. Can you name something in your life that would be harder without the inventions you read about?

_____

_____

_____

_____

8. How did discoveries and advances in the Islamic empire help people in other parts of the world?

_____

_____

_____

_____

Reading

Food and Baghdad

1. How many recipes did Ibn Sayyar al-Warraq compile in his book of recipes?

   _____

2. Name all the ingredients in the sample recipe under "Food of the Classical Age," on page 63 of the Reader.

   _____

   _____

   _____

3. If your teacher provided you with a dictionary or encyclopedia, choose at least three of these ingredients that you are not familiar with, look them up to understand what they are, and briefly describe them below.

   Ingredient 1: _____

   Description: _____

   _____

   Ingredient 2: _____

   Description: _____

   _____

Ingredient 3: _____

Description: _____

_____

Ingredient 4: _____

Description: _____

_____

4. In the sample recipe, what clues can you find suggesting that Muslims were concerned not just with how their food tasted, but also with how it looked?

_____

_____

_____

5. Reread the first paragraph of "The Great City of Baghdad," on page 65. a) What features of Baghdad prevented unwanted people from entering the city, and b) What features of Baghdad allowed people to enter and exit the city?

_____

_____

_____

6. What architectural feature of the caliph's palace is also found on many mosques?

_____

7. Can you find the sentence from "The Great City of Baghdad" that suggests the importance of cleanliness to people in the city?

_____

_____

_____

8. What feature of the palace was said to provide a warning of attacks?

_____

_____

_____

9. What is the architectural term for the tower shown in picture 3?

_____

_____

_____

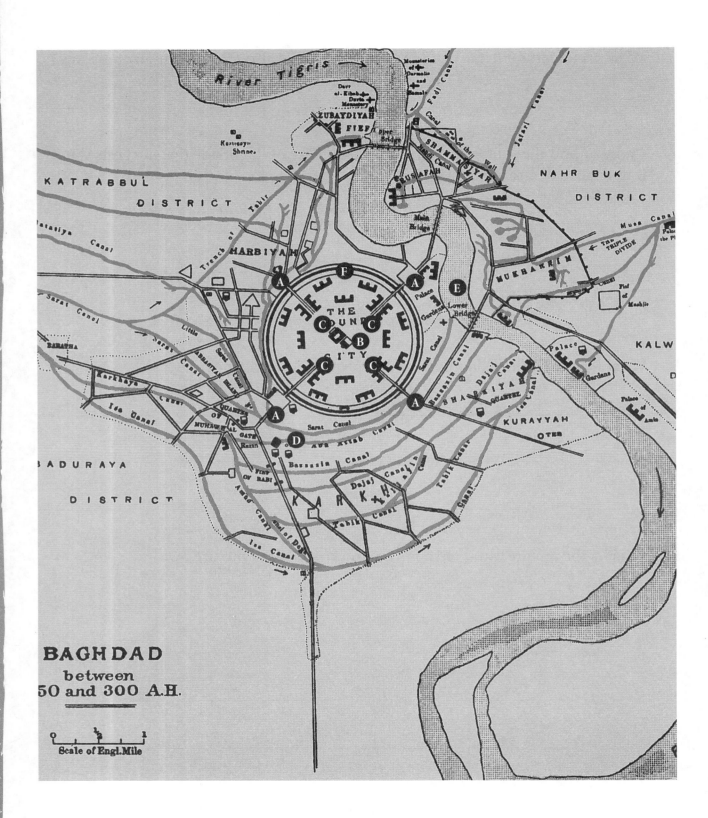

Match each of the city features below with the correct letter on the map.

_____ four great gates

_____ caliph's palace

_____ four huge streets

_____ houses for caliph's family, staff, and servants

_____ moat formed from Tigris River

_____ thick mud brick walls

NAME: _____ DATE: _____

Writing

Classical Age Graphic Organizer

My group's research topic:_____

Facts	Notes for Paraphrasing
Fact Number 1.	
Fact Number 2.	
Fact Number 3.	
Fact Number 4.	
Fact Number 5.	

Presentation Sentences

NAME: _____ DATE: _____

1. **refined,** *v.* improved (**59**)

2. **foundation,** *n.* basis (**59**)

3. **algebra,** *n.* a branch of mathematics (**59**)

4. **astronomy,** *n.* the study of stars and planets (**59**)

5. **hygiene,** *n.* clean conditions that promote health (**61**)

6. **bathhouses,** *n.* buildings for bathing (**61**)

7. **pioneered,** *v.* was among the first to explore or accomplish something (**61**)

8. **canon,** *n.* a collection of rules and knowledge (**61**)

9. **sophisticated,** *adj.* complex (**61**)

10. **practical,** *adj.* useful (**61**)

11. **arcades,** *n.* covered passageways (**65**)

12. **communal,** *adj.* shared by a community (**65**)

Reading

1. According to what you read, how did the Christian army of the First Crusade treat the inhabitants of Jerusalem?

   _____

   _____

2. What action by the Seljuks was one cause of the Crusades?

   _____

   _____

3. Who were the "Sultan's enemies" (page 68), according to the Jewish man's letter?

   _____

   _____

4. The fall of what city into Muslim hands prompted the Second Crusade?

   _____

   _____

NAME: _____   DATE: _____

Writing

Classical Age Opening Statement

Draft an opening statement to discuss with your group. Remember:

–Your opening statement should explain what you will be talking about.

–Your opening statement should be interesting and make the listener want to hear more about your subject.

–You can use an imaginary scenario, but you cannot make up facts.

My Draft Opening Statement:

_____

_____

_____

_____

Our Group's Opening Statement:

_____

_____

_____

_____

1. **rousing**, *adj.* exciting (**66**)

2. **access,** *v.* approach; use (**67**)

3. **jockeying,** *v.* competing for (**67**)

4. **waned,** *v.* faded (**68**)

5. **figurehead,** *n.* a person who holds the title of head of a group, but has no real power (**68**)

6. **fractured,** *adj.* broken, split (**68**)

7. **rampage,** *n.* violent, destructive behavior (**68**)

8. **barracks,** *n.* housing for soldiers (**70**)

9. **intensively,** *adv.* with great effort (**70**)

10. **elite,** *adj.* the choice or best of anything (**70**)

11. **valiant**, *adj.* brave (**72**)

12. **finance,** *v.* provide money for (**72**)

13. **bewildered,** *adj.* confused (**73**)

14. **beset,** *v.* attacked; surrounded (**73**)

15. **agitated,** *adj.* upset (**73**)

16. **pageboys,** *n.* young messengers (**74**)

17. **chivalry,** *n.* a code of honor often connected to European knights of the Middle Ages (**74**)

NAME: _____ DATE: _____

Grammar

For items 1–3, fill in the blanks to add an <u>adjective</u> and <u>adverb</u> to each sentence.

1. Jane _____ bounced in her seat as he listened to tunes through his
              (adverb)

    _____ headphones.
       (adjective)

2. Blanche _____ kissed her puppy goodbye before boarding the
             (adjective)

    _____ bus to summer camp.
       (adverb)

3. After seeing his _____ sister on his bicycle, Alejandro _____
              (adjective)   (adverb)

    yelled at her to get off.

For items 4–6, identify whether the sentence fragment is missing a <u>subject</u> or a <u>predicate</u>. Then add a subject or predicate to make the sentence complete.

4. pleased to meet you

    The sentence fragment is missing a _____.

    Complete sentence: _____

5. seventy alien spaceships

    The sentence fragment is missing a _____.

    Complete sentence: _____

    _____

6. the lonely bear

The sentence fragment is missing a _____.

Complete sentence: _____

_____

Underline the three run-on sentences in the paragraph below. Then, for items 7–9, rewrite these run-ons as grammatically correct sentences.

The Muslims wanted their mosques to be beautiful, imposing, and noticeable from afar one of their greatest architectural innovations was the pointed arch. A pointed arch is very graceful, but it also bears a lot of weight. In addition to arches, many of the mosques had great domes people looked up at the huge dome and felt as if they were looking at heaven. The domes inspired awe in the worshippers. Perhaps because they did not believe in representing Muhammad's face, other decorative elements became more important these elements included geometric patterns. Artists inscribed squares or triangles inside circles and interlocked the figures into patterns that could be almost endlessly repeated. These patterns were intended to remind viewers of the infinite expanse of the universe.

7. _____

_____

_____

8. _____

_____

_____

9. _____

_____

_____

For items 10–13, write the sentence described, and identify the sentence type.

Example:

Write a sentence asking about the depth of the swimming pool.

How deep is the pool?

Sentence Type: *interrogative*

10. Write a sentence asking your teacher for extra homework.

_____

_____

Sentence Type: _____

11. Write a sentence telling a friend that the movie you saw last night was your favorite movie of all time.

_____

_____

Sentence Type: _____

12. Write a sentence telling a classmate to return the book she borrowed.

_____

_____

Sentence Type: _____

13. Write a sentence identifying the three colors of a traffic light.

_____

_____

Sentence Type: _____

Morphology

For items 1–4, choose the word that best completes the sentence. Then write the part of speech of the word you chose.

1. Anika was glad the doctor told her she was _____.
    (*health*/ *healthy*)

    The part of speech of the word I chose is _____.

2. Charlie's dad asked him to oil the door because it was _____.
    (*squeaks*/ *squeaky*)

    The part of speech of the word I chose is _____.

3. We felt a lot of _____on the flight.
    (*bumps*/ *bumpy*)

    The part of speech of the word I chose is _____.

4. Most people in town thought that old miser Madison was _____.
    (*greed*/ *greedy*)

    The part of speech of the word I chose is _____.

For items 5–8, write a sentence using the word provided.

5.   word: *dirt*

_____

_____

6.   word: *dirty*

_____

_____

7.   word: *chill*

_____

_____

8.   word: *chilly*

_____

_____

12.3

NAME: _____   DATE: _____

Spelling

A. List the following fifteen spelling words in alphabetical order. After each word, write the word's part of speech (noun, adjective, or verb).

unafraid	unpleasant	nonviolent
ensure	encourage	monarch
matriarch	patriarch	squeaky
paragraph	autograph	graphite
calligraphy	telegraph	biography

1. _____ part of speech: _____

2. _____ part of speech: _____

3. _____ part of speech: _____

4. _____ part of speech: _____

5. _____ part of speech: _____

6. _____ part of speech: _____

7. _____ part of speech: _____

8. _____ part of speech: _____

9. _____ part of speech: _____

10. _____ part of speech: _____

11. _____ part of speech: _____

12. _____ part of speech: _____

13. _____ part of speech: _____

14. _____ part of speech: _____

15. _____ part of speech: _____

B. What does the root word **graph** mean?

_____

C. What does the root word **arch** mean?

_____

D. What does the prefix **un**– mean?

_____

E. What does the prefix **non**– mean?

_____

F. Adding the suffix –**y** to a word usually turns that word into what part of speech?

_____

Reading

1. Why does the crane consider his life to be drab?

   _____

   _____

   _____

2. The expression "without having to lift a finger" means "without putting in any effort."

   A. How does the author change this expression in the second paragraph of "The Crane and the Crab"?

   _____

   _____

   _____

   B. Why does the author make this change?

   _____

   _____

   _____

3. The first sentence on page 80 is: "The crab was as good as her word." In the space below, paraphrase both the sentence <u>before</u> and the sentence <u>after</u> "The crab was as good as her word." Then use context clues to define the expression "as good as her word." Explain how you reached your answer.

    _____

    _____

    _____

    _____

    _____

4. Why does the crane have to force himself to remain calm when the fish come to the surface?

    _____

    _____

    _____

5. Why does the king of the fishes fling himself into the crane's beak?

    _____

    _____

    _____

NAME: _____ DATE: _____

6.   Why does the crab call the crane a "monster" (page 82)?

_____

_____

_____

7.   Review the definition of the word *cunning*. Why does the crane feel "less cunning by the minute" (page 83)?

_____

_____

_____

Writing

Group Number _____

Our Group's Topic: _____

A. Our Group's Opening Statement:

_____

_____

_____

_____

B. My Presentation Sentence(s):

_____

_____

_____

_____

C. Our Group's Concluding Statement:

_____

_____

_____

_____

_____

The Names and Order of Our Presenters:

1. Opening Statement Presenter:

2. Next Presenter:

3. Next Presenter:

4. Next Presenter:

5. Next Presenter:

6. Next Presenter:

7. Concluding Statement Presenter:

Writing

Islamic Classical Age Presentation

Draft a conclusion below to discuss with your group. Remember that your conclusion should:

- Sum up what you've said in a few lines

- Be interesting to the listener, and make them want to hear more about the subject

You may wish to use one of the following phrases to begin your conclusion:

- "In conclusion"

- "To sum up"

- "To finish our presentation"

My Conclusion:

_____

_____

_____

_____

_____

NAME: _____   DATE: _____

1. **folktales,** *n.* traditional stories that came back from a particular group or culture (**77**)

2. **cunning,** *adj.* clever; sneaky (**78**)

3. **drab,** *adj.* boring (**78**)

4. **stalking,** *v.* hunting for (**78**)

5. **lazing,** *v.* relaxing (**78**)

6. **cultivate,** *v.* develop (**78**)

7. **air,** *n.* appearance (**78**)

8. **scuttled,** *v.* ran with hasty steps (**78**)

9. **offense,** *n.* insult (**79**)

10. **pondered,** *v.* thought about (**79**)

11. **smug,** *adj.* feeling confident and superior (**82**)

12. **proceedings,** *n.* happenings (**82**)

13. **obliged,** *v.* did a favor (**82**)

14. **bleaching,** *v.* making white by exposing to the sun or a chemical (**82**)

15. **pincers,** *n.* claws (**83**)

16. **departed,** *adj.* dead (**83**)

17. **comrades,** *n.* friends (**83**)

Writing

Title of Fable: _____

A. Moral:_____

B. Animal Characters (each fable should have at least two)

Animal 1:_____

Personification:_____

Animal 2:_____

Personification:_____

Animal 3:_____

Personification:_____

C. Events (each fable should have at least four)

1. _____

   _____

2. _____

   _____

3. _____

_____

4. _____

_____

5. _____

_____

6. _____

_____

Events in "The Crane and the Crab"

1. The crane hatches a plan so that he will not have to hunt for fish anymore.

2. The crane and the crab speak about the fishermen and saving the fish.

3. The crab talks to the fish, and the fish listen to the crane's plan.

4. The crane safely carries the king of the fish to the new pond and back again.

5. The crane eats the next two fish on the way to the new pond.

6. After the crane picks up the crab and threatens to eat her, the crab grabs him by the neck and sends him away forever.

Reading

Group 1

Title of Fable: _____

Moral of Fable: _____

_____

Group 2

Title of Fable: _____

Moral of Fable: _____

_____

Group 3

Title of Fable: _____

Moral of Fable: _____

_____

Group 4

Title of Fable: _____

Moral of Fable: _____

_____

NAME: _____ DATE: _____

Group 5

Title of Fable: _____

Moral of Fable: _____

_____

Group 6

Title of Fable: _____

Moral of Fable: _____

_____

Morphology

Change the root words below into adjectives by affixing them with the suffix –y. Then use the adjective in a sentence. Remember that in adding the suffix –y to words that end in an e, the e is dropped.

Example:

Word: *ease*

Adjective: _easy_____

After training all summer, swimming across the lake was easy.

1. Word: *chill*

   Adjective: _____

   _____

   _____

2. Word: *smell*

   Adjective: _____

   _____

   _____

3. Word: *juice*

   Adjective: _____

   _____

   _____

4. Word: *dirt*

    Adjective: _____

    _____

    _____

5. Word: *shine*

    Adjective: _____

    _____

    _____

6. Word: *rain*

    Adjective: _____

    _____

    _____

7. Word: *curl*

    Adjective: _____

    _____

    _____

Spelling

Write the correct spelling word on the blank line to complete each sentence. Words cannot be used more than once, and some words will not be used at all. You may need to add suffixes, such as –s, –es, –ed, or –ing, to the words to complete the sentences.

unafraid	monarch	autograph
unpleasant	matriarch	graphite
nonviolent	patriarch	calligraphy
ensure	squeaky	telegraph
encourage	paragraph	biography

1. When accepting the award, the actress thanked her parents, who always

    _____ her to follow her dreams.

2. Grandma Thelma makes all the family decisions, because she is the

    _____.

3. The leaders of the two countries tried to find a _____ way

    to settle the border dispute.

4. The spy kept turning around to _____ that nobody was

    following him.

5. The elderly _____ hoped her daughter would rule after her.

6. The writer did not explain his main idea until the sixth _____.

7. The pup loved playing with his _____ toy, but the noise
    started getting on my nerves.

8. After studying all weekend, she was _____ to take the test.

Write sentences using spelling words of your choice that were not used in the first eight sentences. Be sure to use correct capitalization and punctuation.

9. _____

_____

10. _____

_____

11. _____

_____

12. _____

_____

NAME: _____ DATE: _____

Spelling

Spelling Assesment

Write the spelling words as your teacher calls them out.

1. _____

2. _____

3. _____

4. _____

5. _____

6. _____

7. _____

8. _____

9. _____

10. _____

11. _____

12. _____

13. _____

14. _____

15. _____

Unit Assessment: Islamic Empires in the Middle Ages

Reading

Today you will read two selections related to the Islamic empires. Read the first selection, and answer the questions about it. Then read the second selection, and answer the questions about it. Some of the questions have two parts. Note that the sections' paragraphs are numbered along the right-hand margin for easy reference.

Two Great Doctors of the Islamic Classical Age

The Classical Age of Islam was a time of great progress in many fields, including science, mathematics, poetry, and art. Some of the most important advances of the Classical Age, however, were in the field of medicine. Two men, who lived thousands of miles apart at opposite ends of the Islamic empire, stand out as two of the most important physicians of the Middle Ages.   **1**

The first of these men, Abu al-Qasim Al-Zahrawi (also known as Albucasis), was born in the western part of the empire in 936, in the city of Córdoba, which today is in Spain. Some of his most important contributions to medicine were in the area of surgery. His book *On Surgery and Instruments* was an illustrated guide that provided step-by-step diagrams of how to perform different operations and what tools to use. Among the surgical instruments he invented were tools to remove objects from his patients' throats and ears. Some of the instruments he introduced are still being used today, including a thread that doctors use to stitch up internal organs.   **2**

Albucasis also wrote important works about dentistry, childbirth, and the ingredients that go into different medicine. The personal side of being a doctor was also very important to him. He encouraged the medical students he taught to have good relationships with their patients and to give them all individual attention. In addition, he believed that rich and poor alike deserved the same treatment from doctors.   **3**

The other great doctor of the Islamic Classical Age was Ibn Sina, who was born around the year 980 in Central Asia, which is in the eastern part of the Islamic empire. He was a very intelligent child with an amazing memory. In fact, by the age of ten he had memorized the entire Qur'an. As a teenager, he spent years studying the works of the Greek philosopher Aristotle; he turned to medicine at the age of sixteen.   **4**

Ibn Sina's most famous book, *The Canon of Medicine*, was translated into many languages and studied by physicians all over the world, even hundreds of years after his death. Today we still follow much of Ibn Sina's advice about setting broken bones and staying healthy through exercise, a nutritious diet, and by getting plenty of sleep. He even wrote about the   **5** best methods to use when testing new medicines. And, like Albucasis, Ibn Sina believed that everyone was entitled to good medical care. He treated many patients without asking for payment.   **5**

Ibn Sina's writings and teachings were not limited to medicine. In addition to being an outstanding doctor and teacher of doctors, he wrote about many other scientific subjects, including chemistry, physics, and astronomy. He was even a poet and a judge!   **6**

Of course, the science of medicine has advanced greatly since the time of Albucasis and Ibn Sina. Some of their methods might seem very "unscientific" in modern times. But the fact that some of their practices are still used today is a reminder that these two men were very great doctors.   **7**

1. The text tells us that Albucasis and Ibn Sina lived thousands of miles from each other. What does this teach us about the Islamic empire?

_____

_____

Use the following chart to compare and contrast Albucasis and Ibn Sina.

		Albucasis	**Ibn Sina**
2.	Born where?		
3.	Most famous book?		
4.	An important contribution?		

5. What opinion regarding medical treatment for the poor was shared by both Albucasis and Ibn Sina?

_____

6. In paragraph 1, the text describes two of the most important physicians of the Middle Ages. In paragraph 6, the text states that Ibn Sina's book was studied by physicians all over the world. What is a synonym for physician?

   a. scientist

   b. patient

   c. doctor

   d. author

7. Which of the following is the best evidence to support the statement that Albucasis and Ibn Sina were great doctors?

   a. They were alive during the Classical Age of Islam.

   b. They introduced practices that are still in use today.

   c. They wrote books.

   d. They had students.

Bashar Remembers the Battle of Yarmouk

I was only a boy, but I was old enough to be afraid as I peered through the branches at the enemy. Of course, I had confidence in General Abu Ubayda and great faith in Islam and our prophet, Muhammad. I had even heard the prophet speak in person during his final pilgrimage to Mecca. His message of believing in the one true God, living a humble life, and being generous toward the poor was fair and just. My parents were the ones who decided our family would follow the path of Islam, but my faith was as strong as theirs.

1

Still, my faith could not drive the fear from my stomach. The word spreading around the camp was that the Byzantine army was 100,000 men strong. I had never seen 100,000 of anything, so I climbed a tree to take a look for myself. What I saw were rows and rows of Byzantine soldiers stretching to the horizon. There were far too many men to count, but it was clear that we were greatly outnumbered.

2

And it was not only the numbers that made me afraid. The Byzantine army was famous for its great cavalry, skilled archers, and fearless swordsmen. Just a few months ago, many of our soldiers had been herding livestock, trading spices, or tanning animal skins to make leather. How could these simple tribesmen stand up to the greatest fighting force in the world? General Abu Ubayda had even made my own father a captain—my gentle father, who spoke to young camels like they were children and nursed an injured bird until its wing had healed. He was supposed to lead men against such a powerful foe?

3

The first two days of battle confirmed my worst fears. The shouts from the battlefield were terrifying. Hundreds of wounded soldiers limped weakly back into camp. Together with the other children, I spent every waking minute fetching water for the injured men and cutting tent cloth into strips for bandages. Our only rest came when we stopped briefly to pray five times a day.

4

Just as we were finishing our sunset prayer on the second day, it began. It started with just a trickle of men, but soon, along with all the women and children of the camp, I watched as thousands of husbands, fathers, and brothers stumbled toward us. They had defeat written on their faces. Our entire army was retreating. My heart sank. "This is the end," I thought. My faith was still strong, but I was sure that the Byzantines had won.

5

I was wrong. As the men staggered forward, the mothers, wives, and daughters of the camp turned the tide of history. As if with one voice, they shouted at the men, urging them to turn around and fight. They threw rocks and charged at them with tent poles. Perhaps it seems cruel, but the women understood that if the men retreated now, the Muslim army would surely lose. The wounded were allowed back into camp, but from that point forward, every able-bodied man knew that victory was the only choice. Without complaint, the men returned to the field and fought bravely. Although the battle raged for four more days, the outcome was no longer in doubt. One empire was falling, and a new one was on the rise.

6

8. What do the following sentences from paragraph 3 tell the reader about the Muslim and Byzantine armies?

> Just a few months ago, many of our soldiers had been herding livestock, trading spices, or tanning animal skins to make leather. How could these simple tribesmen stand up to the greatest fighting force in the world?

a. The soldiers of the Muslim army had experience that would be useful against the Byzantine army.

b. The soldiers of the Muslim army worked harder than the soldiers of the Byzantine army.

c. The Muslim army was the greatest fighting force in the world, and the Byzantine army was made up of simple tribesmen.

d. The soldiers of the Muslim army did not have the skills and experience of the Byzantine army.

. **Part A:** Write a sentence describing the soldiers of the Muslim army.

_____

_____

_____

Part B: Write a sentence describing the soldiers of the Byzantine army.

_____

_____

_____

Part C: Write a sentence comparing the soldiers of the Muslim army to the soldiers of the Byzantine army.

_____

_____

_____

10. After describing his fears, Bashar states, in paragraph 4, that the first two days of the battle "confirmed" his worst fears. What does he mean?

    a. He means that his fears were coming true.

    b. He means that he should not have been afraid.

    c. He means that he forgot why he had been afraid.

    d. He means that his fears were becoming much worse.

11. In paragraph 5, Bashar states, "Just as we were finishing our sunset prayer on the second day, it began." What began?

    a. the battle of Yarmouk

    b. The wounded limped into camp.

    c. the sunset prayer

    d. the retreat of the Muslim men

12. In paragraph 6, Bashar states that "one empire was falling and a new one was on the rise."

    Part A: What empire was falling?

    _____

    Part B: What empire was on the rise?

    _____

NAME: _____ DATE: _____

Grammar

For item 13, write "n." above the nouns in the sentence and "adj." above the adjectives in the sentence. Then draw an arrow from each adjective to the noun it describes.

13. The new caliph opened his grand palace to rich and poor people.

For item 14, write a sentence using the verb and adverb provided.

14. verb: *marched*
    adverb: *slowly*

_____

_____

_____

For item 15, correct the run-on sentence by turning it into two complete sentences.

15. King Richard the Lionheart led the crusaders his goal was to recapture Jerusalem.

_____

_____

_____

For item 16, indicate whether the sentence fragment is missing a subject or a predicate.

16. studied in Baghdad during the Classical Age.

    The sentence is missing a: _____

    (subject / predicate)

For items 17, 18, 19, and 20, circle the sentence type that best describes the sentence.

17. Give me a saddle for my camel.

    declarative   interrogative   imperative   exclamatory

18. What time does the caravan arrive?

    declarative   interrogative   imperative   exclamatory

19. I ate a banana yesterday.

    declarative   interrogative   imperative   exclamatory

20. It's freezing in here!

    declarative   interrogative   imperative   exclamatory

Morphology

21.　**Part A:** Which of the following words is a synonym for *unusual*?

　　a.　special

　　b.　ordinary

　　c.　broken

　　d.　similar

Part B: Which of the following words in an antonym for *unusual*?

　　a.　special

　　b.　ordinary

　　c.　broken

　　d.　similar

22.　Write the correct word to complete the sentence.

　　I took all the _____things out of my pack so that it would
　　　　　　(violent / nonviolent / essential / nonessential)
　　be lighter.

23.　Write a sentence using the word *unpleasant*. The sentence should demonstrate the
　　meaning of the word.

　　_____

　　_____

　　_____

24. Write a sentence using the word *ensure*. The sentence should demonstrate the meaning of the word.

_____

_____

_____

25. **Part A**: What does the root word *graph* mean?

    a. something spoken

    b. something written or drawn

    c. something eaten

    d. something that repeats

    Part B: What does the word *matriarch* mean?

    a. the male leader of a church

    b. the female leader of a church

    c. the male leader of a family

    d. the female leader of a family

Islamic Empires in the Middle Ages End-of-Unit Content Assessment

The following question has two parts. Answer Part A first, and then answer Part B.

1. The Reader states that "Muhammad was born at a time of enormous change."

    Part A: Which of the following quotes supports this statement?

    a. "The Roman Empire became too big to govern, splitting into two.

    b. "The Roman Empire had dominated for centuries."

    c. "Arabia benefited from Byzantine trade."

    d. "For many centuries, the West had traded with the East."

    Part B: Which of the following quotes does not support this statement?

    a. "The Roman Empire became too big to govern, splitting into two."

    b. "Over time, the Western Empire collapsed, and Medieval Europe emerged."

    c. "While Western Europe became Christian, other powers and ideas arose in the rest of the former Roman Empire.

    d. "For many centuries, the West had traded with the East."

For items 2–6 read each of the following statements from the Reader, and decide whether it describes life in the Arabian Desert or life in the city of Mecca.

2. "Life was harsh and dangerous in the arid Arabian climate, and without a regular supply of water, families could not survive and settle in one place."

    Arabian Desert   Mecca

3. "Finding enough water...to survive was a constant struggle, and there were barely enough crops and cattle to feed everyone."

    Arabian Desert   Mecca

4. "People bustl[ed] through the streets, [and] merchants shout[ed] about their wares."

                    Arabian Desert   Mecca

5. "Rich and poor liv[ed] side by side."

                    Arabian Desert   Mecca

6. "At night…the sky is very clear, and the temperature plummets."

                    Arabian Desert   Mecca

7. Which of the following did not occur during the first eight years of Muhammad's life?

    a. Muhammad was sent to live among the Bedouins.

    b. Muhammad become his uncle's closest advisor.

    c. Muhammad's grandfather died.

    d. Muhammad was separated from his foster family.

8. Of what city did Muhammad become arbiter in 622?

    a. Damascus

    b. Yathrib

    c. Córdoba

    d. Baghdad

9. What title did Muhammad's successors take?

    a. prophet

    b. sultan

    c. general

    d. caliph

10. Whom did the Muslims fight at the Battle of Yarmouk?

    a. the crusaders

    b. the Byzantines

    c. the Sunnis

    d. the Persians

For items 11–13, fill in the answer that best completes the sentence. For items 14–17, circle the letter of the answer that best completes the sentence.

11. Shiite and Sunni Muslims disagreed over _____.

    a. whether Mecca should be the capital of the Islamic empire

    b. strategy at the Battle of Yarmouk

    c. who should have been caliph

    d. the amount non-Muslims should be taxed

12. After the civil war, _____ ruled the Islamic empire for almost one hundred years.

    a. the Umayyads

    b. Uthman

    c. the Byzantines

    d. the crusaders

13. The Dome of the Rock is located in _____.

    a. Spain

    b. Mecca

    c. Medina

    d. Jerusalem

14. What city served as the capital of the Islamic empire during the Classical Age?

a. Damascus

b. Baghdad

c. Jerusalem

d. Constantinople

15. Which of the following was a characteristic of Islamic architecture?

a. flat roofs

b. detailed portraits of Muhammad

c. pointed arches

d. large tapestries

16. Which of the following was one of the causes of the Crusades?

a. Muslim Turks did not allow Christian pilgrims to visit Jerusalem.

b. The Islamic world was wealthier than Europe.

c. The Muslim armies were exhausted.

d. Jews, Christians, and Muslims co-existed in great cities.

17. What were the caliphs' specially trained soldiers called?

a. the cavalry

b. the Mamluks

c. the crusaders

d. the champions

Match the items from the column on the left with their description on the right. Write the letter on the line.

_____ Umar

a. the holy book of Islam

_____ Saladin

b. Muhammad's son-in-law who served as caliph

_____ *The Canon of Medicine*

c. caliph who was said to favor his own family and clan

_____ Ali

d. led the Muslims against the Christians in the Third Crusade

_____ the Qur'an

e. a book written during the Islamic Classical Age

_____ Uthman

f. caliph who collected taxes to help the poor

24. Circle the two sentences below in which the word *plummeted* is used correctly.

   a. After the countdown, the rocket plummeted toward outer space.

   b. Before opening his parachute, the skydiver plummeted toward Earth.

   c. Over the course of several days, the helium balloon slowly plummeted to the floor.

   d. The pitcher's fastball plummeted in a straight line toward home plate.

   e. When the temperature plummeted in the morning, I wished I had brought lighter clothes.

   f. When the temperature plummeted at night, I wished I had brought a warm coat.

25. Which of the words in the sentence above provides the best clue as to the meaning of the word *shrine*?

> "The Kaaba (the "cube") was a famous shrine in Mecca that Muhammad's tribe, the Quraysh, looked after and where its members worshipped their gods."

a. Muhammad's tribe, the Quraysh

b. the "cube"

c. looked after

d. its members worshipped their gods

Adjectives and Adverbs

For items 1–5, fill in the blanks to add an adjective and adverb to each sentence.

1. King Richard _____ grabbed his_____

         adv.   adj.

sword when he heard that the Muslims were attacking.

2. Kasim _____ led his camel to the _____

     adv.   adj.

watering hole for a drink.

3. The _____ student _____ returned to

     adj.   adv.

school after a great vacation.

4. Erin _____walked to the party, because she did not want to

    adj.

miss any of the _____ snacks.

         adv.

5. The roads were _____, so Leanne drove _____.

         adj.   adv.

Subjects and Predicates

For items 6–10, underline the subject, and circle the predicate.

6. Todd and his brother borrowed each other's clothes.

7. Millions of Muslims traveled to Mecca.

8. Sue promised to come right home after school.

9. The snow had melted by morning.

10. The plane took off about twenty minutes late.

Sentence Fragments

For items 1–10, identify whether the sentence fragment is missing a subject or a predicate. Then add a subject or predicate to make the sentence complete.

Example:

enjoyed their time in the desert

The sentence is missing a _____.

Complete sentence:

The children from the city enjoyed their time in the desert.

1. a strong wind

    The sentence is missing a_____ .

    Complete sentence: _____

    _____

2. the leader of the caravan

    The sentence is missing a_____ .

    Complete sentence: _____

    _____

3. found a dollar between the sofa cushions

    The sentence is missing a_____ .

    Complete sentence: _____

    _____

4. thousands of Byzantine soldiers

The sentence is missing a_____ .

Complete sentence: _____

_____

5. slowly rowed across the lake

The sentence is missing a_____ .

Complete sentence: _____

_____

6. the camels and the hyenas

The sentence is missing a_____ .

Complete sentence: _____

_____

7. recited poems around a fire every night

The sentence is missing a_____ .

Complete sentence: _____

_____

8. eggs and peanut butter

   The sentence is missing a_____ .

   Complete sentence: _____

   _____

9. dug ditches from dawn until dark

   The sentence is missing a_____ .

   Complete sentence: _____

   _____

10. pushed all the buttons in the elevator

   The sentence is missing a_____ .

   Complete sentence: _____

   _____

Run-on Sentences

For items 1–6, correct the run-on sentences by turning each into two complete sentences.

1. The Pope gave a rousing speech he encouraged the Christians to conquer Jerusalem.

   _____

   _____

2. The new caliph was not descended from a relative of Muhammad's the Shias disapproved of him.

   _____

   _____

3. The first eight years of Muhammad's life were filled with tragedy he nevertheless grew up to become a great leader.

   _____

   _____

4. Mr. Cardozo started at our school last year he quickly became my favorite teacher.

   _____

   _____

5. The Roman Empire became too large to govern eventually it split up.

    _____

    _____

6. Estella outgrew her sneakers her mother took her shopping for new ones.

    _____

    _____

There are four run-on sentences in the paragraph below. Underline them, and then in the spaces beneath, rewrite each run-on as two complete sentences.

> Umar was a political genius he established one of the greatest empires in history. Umar won battles and expanded the empire at an even faster rate than Muhammad and Abu Bakr had. He also put structures in place to keep the empire strong he appointed regional governors to the places he conquered and required them to live in a humble way. Umar also created a taxation system for the new Islamic empire all Muslims had to pay a tax of two percent of their earnings to help the poor and needy. Umar was also a military genius. In his ten years as caliph, he won many battles by the time Umar died he had conquered huge portions of Byzantine and Persian territory.

7. Rewrite of First Run-on Sentence:

    _____

    _____

8. Rewrite of Second Run-on Sentence:

_____

_____

9. Rewrite of Third Run-on Sentence:

_____

_____

10. Rewrite of Fourth Run-on Sentence:

_____

_____

Sentence Types

For items 1–4, punctuate the sentences. The sentence type of each is identified.

1. **Declarative:** I prefer sleeping on the bottom bunk

2. **Interrogative:** Who wrote Romeo and Juliet

3. **Imperative:** Please pass the carrots

4. **Exclamatory:** We missed the train

For items 5–8, identify the sentence type.

5. I prefer baloney to salami.

    declarative   interrogative   imperative   exclamatory

6. Were you at soccer practice yesterday?

    declarative   interrogative   imperative   exclamatory

7. I hate roller coasters!

    declarative   interrogative   imperative   exclamatory

8. Text me as soon as you get home.

    declarative   interrogative   imperative   exclamatory

For items 9–13, write a sentence that is of the type indicated and that uses the word provided.

Example:

Sentence type: declarative

Word: *mosque*

Sid admired the dome of the mosque.

9. Sentence Type: declarative

Word: *eagle*

_____

_____

10. Sentence Type: imperative

Word: *now*

_____

_____

11. Sentence Type: exclamatory

Word: *worst*

_____

_____

12. Sentence Type: interrogative

    Word: *birthday*

    _____

    _____

Challenge

    Sentence Type: declarative sentence containing a question

    Word: *wondered*

    _____

    _____

un– and *non*–: Prefixes Meaning "not"

For items 1–8, choose the word below that best completes each sentence. No word should be used more than once. For item 9, follow the instructions given.

living	violent	wrap	usual
nonliving	nonviolent	unwrap	unusual

1. Like many _____ things, plants require air and water.

2. Because he was a _____ boy, Simon chose not to fight with the crusaders.

3. Marisol could not identify the _____ bird she saw outside her window.

4. Mr. Chang did not have time to _____ his daughter's birthday present.

5. This morning, just like every day, I ate my _____ breakfast of cereal and a banana.

6. All this tape is making it difficult to _____ the package.

7. The mad scientist tried to create a breathing human out of _____ parts.

8. A _____ storm tore the roof off our house.

   Challenge: Write a sentence using one of your own *non*– or *un*– words.

_____

–en: Prefix Meaning "to make"

For items 1–6, choose the word below that best completes each sentence. No word should be used more than once. You may need to add –ed, –ing, or –s to make the word work correctly in the sentence. For item 7, answer the question given.

enjoy	endear	enclose	enlarge
ensure	encircle		

1. In order to _____ his house, our neighbor added on a room.

2. A smiling baby is _____ to almost everybody.

3. Mr. Holzman bought extra hotdogs to _____ that everyone would have enough to eat at his cookout.

4. The dog catchers _____ the dog so that she could not escape.

5. Ms. Grumby kept her valuable stamps _____ in an air-tight case.

6. I certainly plan to_____ my summer vacation.

   Challenge: Based on what you know about the prefix *en–* and the root word *trap*, what do you think *entrap* means?

   _____

   _____

   _____

arch: Root Word Meaning "ruler"

For items 1–6, choose the word below that best completes each sentence. No word should be used more than once. You may need to add an –s to make the word work correctly in the sentence. For item 7, follow the instruction given.

matriarch	archrival	monarch
archbishop	hierarchy	anarchy

1. The _____ gave the king advice on matters related to the Church.

2. The caliph was at the very top of the _____ of the Islamic world.

3. After my great-grandmother passed away, my grandmother became the

    _____ of the family.

4. Although Evie and Melanie were best friends, they became_____
    when they played tennis against each other.

5. The _____ dreamed of giving up the throne and living a
    normal life.

6. Some people think that without laws and government, there would be

    _____throughout the land.

7. Write a complete sentence using the word *patriarch*.

    _____

    _____

    _____

graph: Root Word Meaning "something written or drawn"

For items 1–6, choose the word below that best completes each sentence. No word should be used more than once. For item 7, follow the instruction given.

autobiography	calligraphy	cartography
choreography	phonograph	telegraph

1. Colleen had a large collection of maps and atlases; she hoped to study

    _____ one day.

2. In the middle of the nineteenth century, the _____ provided the
    fastest way of sending long-distance messages.

3. The ballet dancer practiced his _____ for several hours every day.

4. The Muslims often decorated their mosques with Arabic_____.

5. Even though we bought him an MP3 player, Grandpa Dwight preferred to play

    music on his old _____.

6. In 1771, Benjamin Franklin started writing his _____.

7. Write a complete sentence using the word *autograph*.

    _____

    _____

    _____

West Africa

<u>Vocabulary</u>

1. **incorporated, *v.*** combined into **(86)**

2. **brocade, *n.*** a cloth woven with an elaborate design **(87)**

3. **native, *adj.*** the place of one's birth **(89)**

4. **millet, *n.*** a type of grain **(91)**

1. The Reader states that West Africans incorporated their own traditions into Islam. Reread the text from the "Kaaba" box, on page 18. How did Muhammad similarly incorporate the traditions of the people of Arabia into Islam?

_____

_____

_____

_____

2. What do you think the people who met King Musa on his pilgrimage to Mecca meant when they said that he "almost put the African sun to shame"? Clue: Think about the color of the sun and about what King Musa carried with him on his pilgrimage.

_____

_____

_____

_____

3. Reread the section "Knowledge in the Classical Age," on page 51. Write an informative paragraph describing similarities between Baghdad and Timbuktu as centers of learning.

_____

_____

_____

_____

4. Imagine that you accompanied Ibn Battuta on his journey, and kept a journal. Write a paragraph describing your favorite or least favorite part of your travels.

_____

_____

_____

_____

Scheherazade

Vocabulary

1. **distress, _n._** pain or sorrow **(94)**

2. **hobbling, _v._** walking slowly, with a limp **(96)**

3. **avenge, _v._** to get revenge **(97)**

4. **culprits, _n._** people guilty of a crime **(99)**

5. **grudgingly, _adv._** in a way that shows reluctance **(100)**

1. The first paragraph on page 94 of the Reader describes the king as follows: "It was whispered that he had once been a good man, but that a romantic tragedy had turned his heart to stone." What does it mean to describe someone as having a heart of stone?

_____

_____

_____

_____

2. Suppose you did not know the meaning of the expression "heart of stone." What context clues in the sentence would help you figure out the definition?

_____

_____

_____

_____

3. Did the vizier approve of Scheherazade's marriage to the king?

_____

_____

_____

_____

4. On page 94, the Reader states that Scheherazade "marched into the palace and to the king." Why do you think the author chose the word *marched* instead of *walked* or *went* or some other verb?

_____

_____

_____

_____

5. On page 102, the young man tells the caliph that "a red mist fell over my eyes." What do you think he means by this? Clue: Think about what emotion is often associated with the color red.

_____

_____

_____

_____

Below, under "Part One," write the first part of a story that is set in the Islamic world in the Middle Ages. Like Scheherazade, end your story at a point that will leave a reader or listener desperate to know what happens next. Then trade activity books with your partner. Under "Part Two," your partner should write the second part of your story, and you should write the second part of your partner's story.

Your Story Title: _____

Part One:

_____

_____

_____

_____

_____

_____

_____

_____

_____

_____

_____

NAME: _____ DATE: _____

_____

_____

_____

_____

_____

_____

_____

_____

_____

_____

_____

_____

_____

_____

Part Two:

_____

_____

_____

_____

_____

_____

_____

_____

_____

_____

_____

_____

_____

_____

NAME: _____ DATE: _____

Amplify.

Core Knowledge Language Arts®

Series Editor-in-Chief

E.D. Hirsch, Jr.

President

Linda Bevilacqua

Editorial Staff

Rachel Wolf, Editorial Director

Professor Ahmed H. al-Rahim,
    Subject Matter Expert and Expert Reviewer

Rosie McCormick, Content Director

Marc Goldsmith, Lead Curriculum Developer

Professor Suleiman Mourad, Expert Reviewer

Dr. Charles C. Haynes, Expert Reviewer

Editorial-Design Coordination

Matthew Ely, Senior Project Manager

Design and Graphics Staff

Todd Rawson, Design Director

Annah Kessler, Visual Designer

Erin O'Donnell, Production Designer

Image Credits